TWO LADS AND A DAD

THE PRODIGAL SON

By Marilyn Lashbrook

Illustrated by Chris Sharp

ME TOO!
READERS

ROPER PRESS, INC.
DALLAS, TEXAS

ME TOO! READERS are designed to help you share the joy of reading with children. They provide a new and fun way to improve a child's reading skills - by practice and example. At the same time, you are teaching your children valuable Bible truths.

Every child thinks about running away from home at some point. The story of the Prodigal Son will help children understand that running away only creates more problems. After reading this book with your children or students, you will have the perfect opportunity to assure them of their importance, of your love for them, and especially of God's love for them. Take time to discuss ways a child can respectfully express his feelings when he is feeling insecure.

Reading is key to successful education. Obeying the principles of God's Word opens the door to a successful life. ME TOO! READERS encourage your children in both!

Bold type: Child reads
Regular type: Adult reads
 :   Wait for child to respond
 :   Talk about it!

Library of Congress Catalog Card Number: 90-63769
ISBN 0-86606-446-X

Art direction and design by
   Chris Schechner Graphic Design

TWO LADS AND A DAD

THE PRODIGAL SON

By Marilyn Lashbrook

Illustrated by Chris Sharp

Taken from Luke 15

ME TOO!
READERS

Once there was a boy who wanted to have fun. He wanted to visit exciting places, meet interesting people, and taste delicious new foods. The boy spent his days dreaming of all the things he would like to do.

But he was the baby of the family. It seemed he was never allowed to do anything. The boy was tired of being told he was too young. "I will run away from home," he said.

One day, the boy went to his father. "I do not want to wait for my share of your money," the boy said. "I want my money now."

His father didn't think it was a good idea, but he knew it was no use to argue. It was time to let his son learn from his own mistakes.

So the father counted all the money. He gave the younger son his share. Soon, the boy packed his things and left home. He wanted to see the world.

The father watched sadly as his boy walked down the road and out of sight. "I love you," whispered the father, "and I will never stop thinking of you."

"Don't waste your tears on that lazy dreamer!" said the older son, "We are lucky to be rid of him."

As the boy hiked down the road, through the forests, and over the mountains, he dreamed of all the exciting things he would see and do. "I'll never be bored again," he said to himself. "From now on, I'm going to have fun, fun, fun.

The boy patted the bag he had stuffed with money. He was sure it would never run out.

"No more chores for me!" he sang out, "Now I'm really free!" And he danced under the sunny blue sky.

The boy traveled day after day, until he came to a country far from home. He made a lot of friends and together they spent his money. They ate the best food and drank lots of wine and bought expensive clothes. And for a little while, the boy had fun.

But soon his money was spent. And there was a famine in the land. Even a little food cost a lot of money.

The boy grew very hungry, but he could not buy any food. His friends forgot all about him once his money was gone. They just had a good time with his money, then left him all alone.

The boy found a job feeding pigs. But he did not make enough to buy the food he needed.

The boy was so hungry, he even thought about eating some of the pig slop. As he watched them eat, his mouth watered.

He looked at the scrubby cobs the hogs were chewing and thought about hot, buttery corn on the cob.

He saw the little pigs slurping up soggy bread crusts. The boy imagined he could smell hot bread baking in the oven.

He watched the sows munching on
rotten apples and remembered the
beautiful fruit trees at home. "Home. I wish
I could go home," the boy said to himself.
"Even my father's servants have more than
enough food to eat. And I'm here starving
to death."

Then the boy had an idea. "I will go home. I will ask my Father to forgive me. Maybe he will let me be one of his servants. I do not deserve to be his son."

So the boy climbed out of the pig sty and stomped the dark, gooey mud from his feet. But the smell of the pigs stayed with him.

It was a long walk home. The boy had a lot to think about.

What did he have to show for all the money he spent? Did his money buy real happiness? Did it buy real friends? ⬣

The world was not at all what he expected. The excitement didn't last. And the price for his fun was just too high.

When the boy was almost home, he looked up and saw someone standing down the road. He looked familiar. Suddenly, the man ran toward the boy. His arms were open wide. Closer and closer he came.

Could it be? Yes! It was the boy's father. And he was smiling.

The man threw his arms around his son and hugged him and kissed him. Before the boy could even apologize, his father shouted to the servants to bring the best clothes in the house.

"Put a robe on my son!" said the father. "And a ring on his finger and sandals on his feet."

"And start cooking!" the boy's father said, "We are going to have a feast. We are going to celebrate!"

The boy went into the house with his father. Servants scurried around getting ready for the celebration. Everybody was excited to have the baby of the family back home.

Well, not quite everybody. When the older brother came in from working in the fields, he heard music and dancing. "What's going on?" he asked one of the servants.

"Come on in!" the servant said, "Your little brother has come home! We are having a feast."

The older brother was angry. "That little runt takes off and plays while I stay here and work. And HE gets the party. Well, I'm not coming!"

The servant went back inside and found the boy's father. "Your older son is outside," the servant whispered . "He is too angry to come in."

The father sighed. "I will go talk to him."

So the man went out to look for his first-born son. When the father found him, he begged his son to come to the party.

"Look!" said his son, "All these years, I've worked hard for you. I've never disobeyed. I've never run away. But have you ever had a party for me? No!"

"You are here with me. You know I love you. You know I am proud of you." said the father, "Everything I have belongs to you!

"But I thought your brother was dead and now he is alive. He was lost. But now he is found. We have to celebrate! This is a happy day for us!

"Please come..." the father began. But his older son just walked away. And the Father watched with tears in his eyes as his son stormed down the road and disappeared from sight.

"I will always love you," the father whispered, "and I will never stop thinking of you."

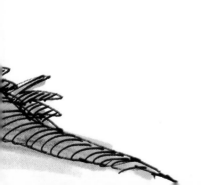

One son stayed home,

One travelled around.

Both boys were lost,

How many were found?

One boy came back,

And admitted his sin.

The other was proud,

and refused to come in.

All people have sinned,

Some big and some small.

God is the father,

Who waits to save all. 🖤🖤

ME TOO!
B O O K S

For Ages 2-5

SOMEONE TO LOVE THE STORY OF CREATION	**"GET LOST LITTLE BROTHER"** THE STORY OF JOSEPH
TWO BY TWO THE STORY OF NOAH'S FAITH	**THE WALL THAT DID NOT FALL** THE STORY OF RAHAB'S FAITH
"I DON'T WANT TO" THE STORY OF JONAH	**NO TREE FOR CHRISTMAS** THE STORY OF JESUS' BIRTH
"I MAY BE LITTLE" THE STORY OF DAVID'S GROWTH	**"NOW I SEE"** THE STORY OF THE MAN BORN BLIND
"I'LL PRAY ANYWAY" THE STORY OF DANIEL	**DON'T ROCK THE BOAT!** THE STORY OF THE MIRACULOUS CATCH
WHO NEEDS A BOAT? THE STORY OF MOSES	**OUT ON A LIMB** THE STORY OF ZACCHAEUS

ME TOO!
R E A D E R S

For Ages 5-8

IT'S NOT MY FAULT MAN'S BIG MISTAKE	**NOTHING TO FEAR** JESUS WALKS ON WATER
GOD, PLEASE SEND FIRE! ELIJAH AND THE PROPHETS OF BAAL	**THE BEST DAY EVER** THE STORY OF JESUS
TOO BAD, AHAB! NABOTH'S VINEYARD	**THE GREAT SHAKE-UP** MIRACLES IN PHILIPPI
THE WEAK STRONGMAN SAMSON	**TWO LADS AND A DAD** THE PRODIGAL SON

Available at your local
bookstore
or from
Roper Press
4737-A Gretna
Dallas, Texas 75207
1-800-284-0158